Smile

Smile

Raina Telgemeier
with color by Stephanie Yue

graphix

An Imprint of

SCHOLASTIC

New York Toronto London Auckland Sydney Mexico City New Delhi Hong Kong

All rights reserved. Published by Graphix, an imprint of Scholastic Inc., *Publishers since 1920.* SCHOLASTIC, GRAPHIX, and associated logos are trademarks and/or registered trademarks of Scholastic Inc. All other trademarks are the property of their respective owners and are used without permission.

No part of this publication may be reproduced, stored in a retrieval system, or transmitted in any form or by any means, electronic, mechanical, photocopying, recording, or otherwise, without written permission of the publisher. For information regarding permission, write to Scholastic Inc., Attention: Permissions Department, 557 Broadway, New York, NY 10012.

This graphic novel is based on personal experiences, though some names have been changed, and certain characters, places, and incidents have been modified in service of the story.

Library of Congress Cataloging-in-Publication Data
Telgemeier, Raina.
Smile / Raina Telgemeier. – 1st ed.
p. cm.
ISBN: 978-0-545-13205-3 (hardcover)
ISBN: 978-0-545-13206-0 (paperback)
1. Youth–Dental care. 2. Girls–Dental care. 3. Self-esteem in adolescence.
4. Beauty, Personal. 5. Graphic novels. I. Title.
RK55.Y68.T45 2010
617.6'45-dc22
2008051782

10 9 8 7 6   15 16 17 18

First edition, February 2010
Edited by Cassandra Pelham
Book design by Phil Falco and John Green
Creative Director: David Saylor
Printed in Singapore   46

For Dave

8

14

19

20

21

22

26

CHAPTER TWO

32

34

WHAT IF WE WAIT TILL AFTER YOUR BIRTHDAY TO GET THEM PIERCED?

YOU ARE GETTING YOUR BRACES PRETTY SOON...

MAYBE THAT COULD BE YOUR REWARD, AND YOUR BIRTHDAY PRESENT.

OKAY!

KAYLAH TOLD ME ABOUT A GOOD JEWELRY PLACE WHERE SHE GOT HERS DONE.

...AN' I SAW THESE FRESH EARRINGS AT CONTEMPO THE OTHER DAY...MELISSA HAS A PAIR OF LIGHT-NING BOLTS...I WANNA GET SOME LIKE BRANDY ON THE NEW MICKEY MOUSE CLUB HAS, TOO...

40

41

43

44

45

48

49

CHAPTER THREE

That summer was pretty normal, as summers go.

Girl Scout Camp

Grandma

Nintendo

Fog

Car trips

Orthodontist

58

IT'S SO STRANGE TO LOOK OUT OVER THE CITY WHEN ALL THE LIGHTS ARE OUT.

AND IT'S SUCH A NICE NIGHT, TOO: CLEAR, WARM, NO WIND, QUIET.

I MIGHT REALLY ENJOY THIS IF IT WEREN'T FOR THE WHOLE "GIGANTIC NATURAL CATASTROPHE" THING...

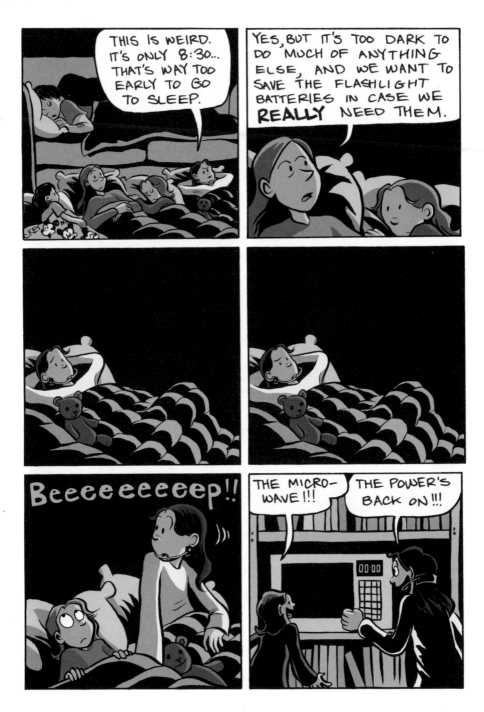

75

CHAPTER FOUR

I even worried during art class, which was usually my escape from reality.

RRIIIIIIIP

REVLON

HEY, MY DAD TOOK ME TO SEE "THE LITTLE MERMAID" LAST NIGHT. IT WAS REALLY GOOD.

OH, YEAH?

YEAH. YOU SHOULD DEFINITELY GO SEE IT.

...MAYBE I WILL.

I'M TAKING YOUR SISTER AND HER FRIEND TO SEE "THE LITTLE MERMAID" TOMORROW, RAINA... WANT TO COME WITH US?

I GUESS.

BUT ONLY 'CAUSE EMILY TOLD ME IT WAS GOOD.

The last day of school came and went.

HAVE A FUN CHRISTMAS!

THANKS... HAVE A NICE HANUKKAH.

Usually, the start of Winter Break is one of the most exciting times of the year.

But that year, everything served as a reminder of what was about to happen to me.

LOOK, GRANDMA GAGNON SENT US A PACKAGE!

OOH, WHAT IS IT?

...PEANUT BRITTLE!

The next morning

MOM!! SHE CAME! THE TOOTH FAIRY CAME!!

"FOR RAINA, FROM THE TOOTH FAIRY"...

HOW COME HER HANDWRITING LOOKS JUST LIKE DAD'S?

107

* FROM NEW KIDS ON THE BLOCK!

CHAPTER FIVE

HIS NAME'S SEAN. HE TRANSFERRED HERE A COUPLE OF MONTHS AGO.

HE'S ON THE JUNIOR BASKETBALL TEAM, AND HE'S REALLY GOOD AT DRAWING.

123 ART

I'M PRETTY SURE HE DOESN'T HAVE A GIRLFRIEND... I'LL HAVE TO FIND OUT!!

OH! UH... HEH HEH... HI!

HI.

YIKES! THAT WAS EMBARRASSING... MY FACE TURNED TOTALLY RED.

I HOPE HE NOTICED!

HEY, RAINA!

112

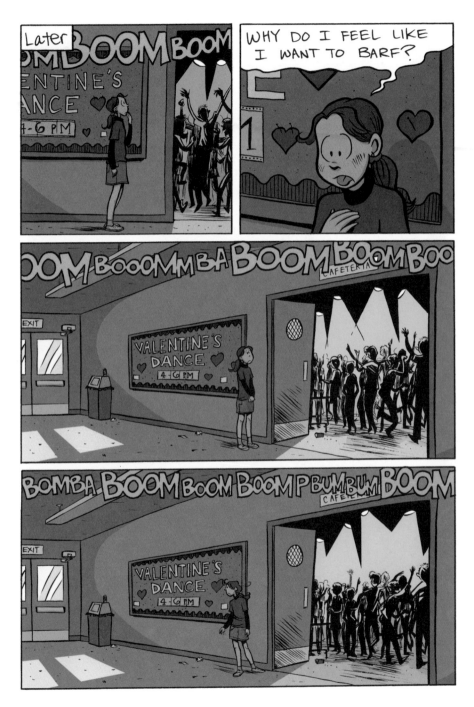

125

Sammy never spoke to me again after that.

Which I guess I deserved.

But I had other things to think about...

And, still others!

EVERYTHING'S LOOKING GREAT! WE CAN GO AHEAD AND PUT YOUR BRACES ON AGAIN SOON!

WHAT?

A BRACE-FACE! I'M GONNA BE A BRACE-FACE AGAIN IN A COUPLE OF WEEKS.

WHICH MEANS I'M GOING TO GO BACK TO LOOKING LIKE A NERD AGAIN.

IT'S SO UNFAIR. I FINALLY GET THIS RETAINER, I FINALLY GET TO LOOK COOL FOR A LITTLE WHILE...

AND NOW I HAVE TO START BACK AT SQUARE ONE!

ACTUALLY, YOU'VE ALWAYS LOOKED LIKE A NERD.

YEAH, "COOL" JUST ISN'T THE WORD TO DE-SCRIBE YOU.

129

Before I knew it, my birthday rolled around again.

OKAY. YOU ARE THIRTEEN YEARS OLD.

I KNOW. IT'S CRAZY!

IT'S TIME YOU KISSED YOUR FIRST BOY, I'D SAY.

HUH?!

COME ON, RAINA. EVERYONE KNOWS YOU HAVE THE HOTS FOR SEAN...

EXCEPT FOR SEAN HIMSELF!

IT'S TIME TO MAKE A MOVE. IT'S TIME TO MAKE AN IMPRESSION.

IT'S TIME FOR A MAKEOVER!!

AAACK! HANG ON! WAIT!!

CABOODLE

GRAB

135

137

WHAT IF IT WAS TRUE? WHAT IF SEAN REALLY WOULD NOTICE ME IF I DRESSED DIFFERENTLY?

WOULD I BE WILLING TO CHANGE, JUST FOR HIM?

SO FAR, BEING A TEENAGER IS NO FUN AT ALL.

As my teeth moved closer together...

The fake teeth in the empty space were shaved down little by little.

By the time eighth grade started, the two fake teeth had been replaced by one fake tooth.

I just hoped no one could tell.

GIRL, YOU NEED TO START USING A BETTER HAIR CONDITIONER.

MY BROTHER HAS THAT SHIRT... IT'S KIND OF A BOY'S SHIRT.

Eighth grade was weird. We were all going through puberty, and at different rates.

Hair suddenly curly

Taller, hips wider

Chest got huge

Acne

Gloomy

Everyone was very preoccupied.

HAIR

CLOTHES

PIMPLES

MAKEUP

DIETING

ETC.

WHATEVER HAPPENED TO TALKING ABOUT CARTOONS?

But, the boys seemed to notice, and acted accordingly.

W-PWING!!!

The only boy who didn't seem to notice what was going on, was... well... guess.

SEAN'S NEVER GOING TO PAY ATTENTION TO YOU. HE'S TOO MUCH OF A BASKETBALL-BRAIN.

IF IT DOESN'T HAVE TO DO WITH THREE-POINTERS OR MICHAEL JORDAN, HE ISN'T INTERESTED.

Girls' Basketball Team
TRYOUTS TODAY

My crush on Sean was old news to everyone else, but it still consumed my thoughts a lot of the time.

15... 36... SEAN...

However, something interesting was starting to happen.

HEY, RAINA!

HEY, KAYLAH. HEY, EDWARD.

YOU GOIN' TO LUNCH?

YEAH, WAIT UP.

YEARBOOK ORDERS

MAY 27th

Some of my friends had kinda-sorta-maybe boyfriends.

Boys who would hang around with us during lunchtime...

... and who would invite their other friends along.

Not all of them were cute, and not all of them were very mature...

WAIT, WHAT'S THIS? NEXT TO MY PEANUT BUTTER SANDWICH?

YAAAAARRGH! SPIDER!!

AIIEEE!!

rubber

But they were good for practice-flirting!

SHOVE!

168

Aptos
Class of 1991
Commencement
Ceremony

June 12, 10:00 AM
Aptos Middle School Auditorium

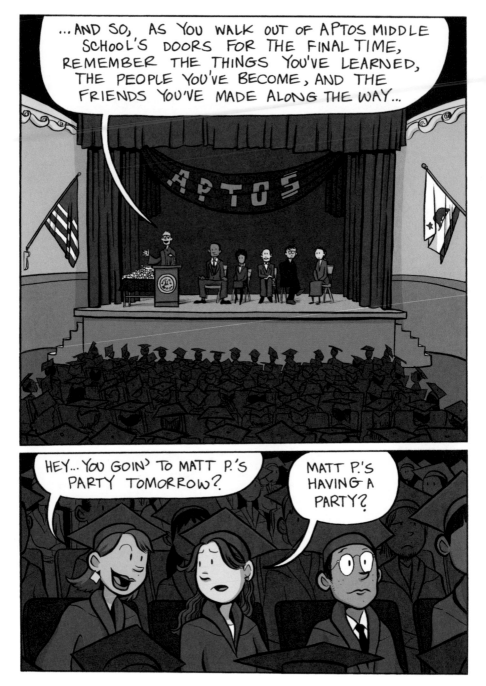

CHAPTER SEVEN

That summer, I was a Girl Scout camp counselor for the last time.

The cutest boy I ever saw was sipping ciiiiiiiider through a straw!

I also sat between my siblings in the car on a couple of long-distance road trips.

MOM!! WILL'S TOUCHING MY FOOT!!

The next stage of my orthodontic treatment was a fairly entertaining one, designed to correct my

CROSS-BITE.

(That's when your top and bottom jaws don't line up.)

To fix this, little hooks are attached to specific brackets on the top and the bottom teeth...

①
②

...and a tiny rubber band is stretched between them.

I CAN' OPEN MA MOUF ALL TH' WEY!

Twannngg!

YOU'LL GET USED TO IT!

183

So, tiny rubber bands joined the contents of my backpack.

0.3

Along with travel toothbrush and paste, dental wax, floss, floss-threaders, a little box of toothpicks, and a tiny bottle of mouthwash.

It was quite the spectacle when I went to get a pencil or whatever.

...OOP!

HA HA! LOOKS LIKE SOMEONE'S TRYING TO COVER UP THEIR DOG BREATH!!

ONE... TWO...

THREE!

SHWWWWP

After that, I essentially "broke up" with my old group of friends.

It was an amicable split— we still said hello in the halls, and acknowledged our shared pasts.

HEY... DID YOU HEAR THAT OUR OLD ART TEACHER DIED?

MS. SHERF? AW, THAT'S SAD.

I was a little lonely now and then, but it didn't bother me.

I was happy to take life at my very own pace.

HA HA!

AND I THOUGHT I WAS (GASP, PANT) THE ONLY SLOW RUNNER IN OUR CLASS!

203

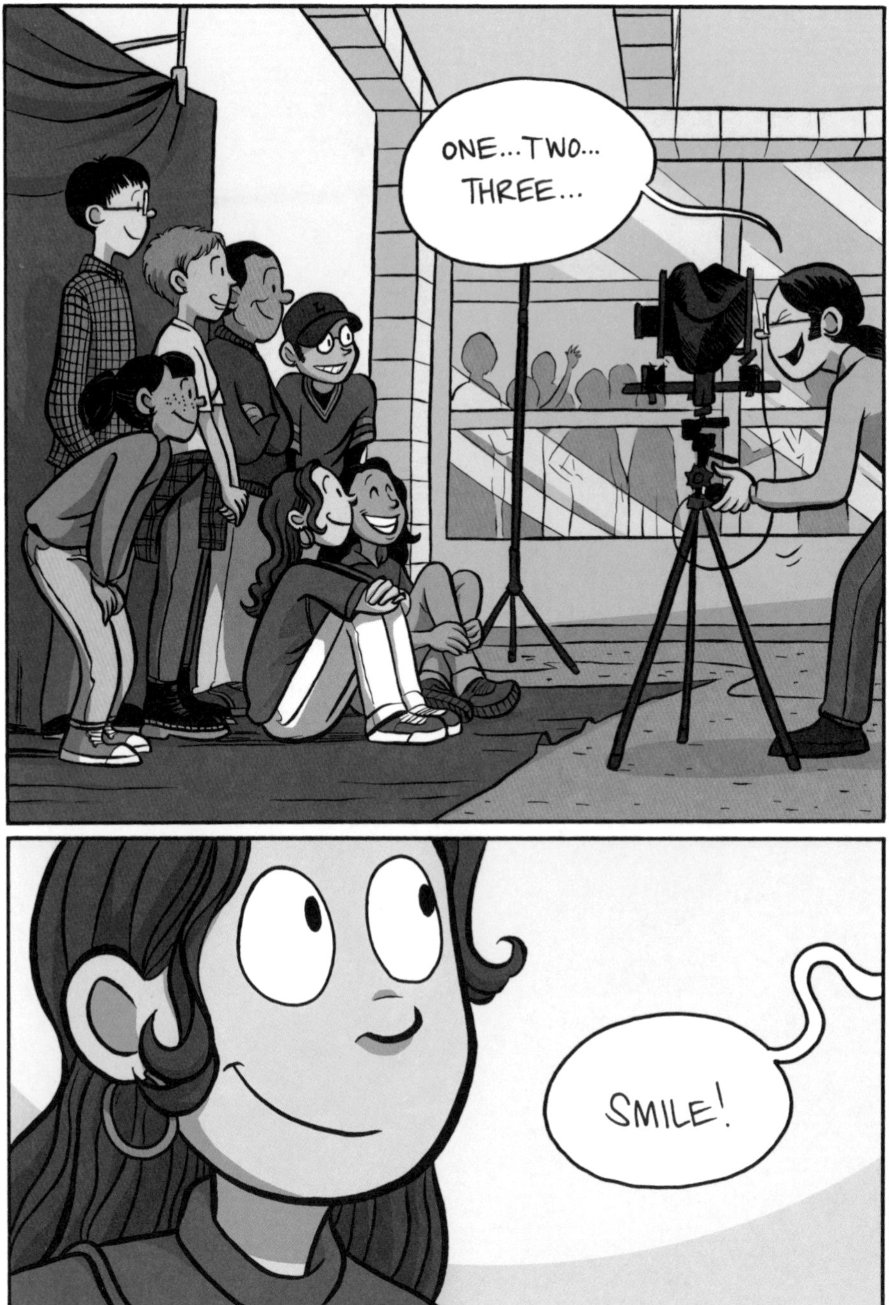
ONE...TWO...
THREE...
SMILE!

The End!

Thanks to...

First and foremost, my husband, Dave Roman, who makes me smile every day.

Mom, Dad, Amara, Will, and Grandma, for being good sports and a great family.

Lea Ada Franco (Hernandez), Joey Manley, and everyone at Girlamatic.com, for giving a home to this project in its infancy. My friend and family dentist, Dr. Anne Spiegel, who evaluated the manuscript and gave me great encouragement along the way. David Saylor and Cassandra Pelham, for being a joy to work with. Phil Falco, John Green, and Stephanie Yue, for helping make my work beautiful. Judy Hansen, for being the best agent I could hope to have.

Alisa Harris, Braden Lamb, Carly Monardo, Craig Arndt, Dalton Webb, Hope Larson, Jordyn Bochon, Kean Soo, Matt Loux, Naseem Hrab, Rosemary Travale, Ryan Estrada, and Yuko Ota, for lending a helping hand during the final stages of production.

All of my friends who wrote me yearbook notes.

Everyone who has shared their own personal dental dramas with me.

The city of San Francisco, for giving me great backgrounds to draw!

Archwired.com, Janna Morishima, Heidi MacDonald, and Barbara Moon, for all their support and enthusiasm over the years.

Theresa Mendoza Pacheco, Marion Vitus, Steve Flack, Alison Wilgus, Zack Giallongo, Gina Gagliano, Bannister, Steve Hamaker, Seth Kushner, Neil Babra, and my extended family, wonderful friends, and readers, who have been invaluable.

Author's Note

I've been telling people about what happened to my teeth ever since I knocked them out in sixth grade. The story had plenty of strange twists and turns, and I found myself saying, "Wait, it gets worse!" a lot. Eventually, I realized I really needed to get it all down on paper.

I had been writing short-story comics for several years, and my tooth tale seemed like a good candidate for a longer narrative comic.

In 2004 I was invited to contribute to a comics-based Web site, Girlamatic.com, and decided to run *Smile* as a weekly Webcomic. This was at the same time I began working on The Baby-sitters Club graphic novels for Scholastic, so the two projects grew and evolved in tandem. By the time I completed the fourth BSC graphic novel, I had drawn, serialized, and posted over 120 pages of *Smile* on the Web!

As I wrote and drew the story, I was able to look back and actually laugh at some of my more painful experiences. What I went through with my teeth wasn't fun, but I lived to tell the tale and came out of it a stronger person. And once *Smile* started to receive reader feedback, I was amazed by how many people had dental stories similar to my own! The process of creating *Smile* has been therapeutic for me, and has also put me in touch with hundreds of kindred spirits. For this I am very grateful.

Even though my smile looks normal now, it's very possible I'll face more dental drama in the future. Amazingly, I'm not afraid of dentists, or dental work. I have a lot of faith and trust in dentistry, and how it can improve people's lives. And on the bright side of things, beyond the work I've had done on my front teeth, I haven't had a cavity since I was six!

Thanks so much for reading.

—Raina

Raina Telgemeier grew up in San Francisco, then moved to New York City, where she earned an illustration degree at the School of Visual Arts. She is the creator of *Smile*, a *#1 New York Times* bestselling graphic memoir based on her childhood. It won a Will Eisner Award for Best Publication for Teens, received a Boston Globe–Horn Book Honor, and has appeared on many state reading lists. She is also the creator of *Drama*, a *#1 New York Times* bestseller, recipient of a Stonewall Book Award Honor, and one of YALSA's Top Ten Great Graphic Novels for Teens. Raina also adapted and illustrated The Baby-sitters Club graphic novels, which were selected for YALSA's Great Graphic Novels for Teens list and *Booklist's* Top 10 Graphic Novels for Youth list.

Raina lives in Astoria, New York, with her husband and fellow cartoonist, Dave Roman. To learn more about Raina, visit her online at www.goRaina.com.